W9-AMT-915

The Life Cycle Library
for Young People

Parents' Answer Book

by Charlotte del Solar, Ph.D.

Published by

PARENT AND CHILD INSTITUTE, CHICAGO

© 1969 by the Parent and Child Institute

Copyright under International Copyright Union.   All Rights Reserved
under Pan American and Universal Copyright Conventions

Printed in United States of America

Contents

1

A Talk
with Parents

Rather than encourage you to read the *Parents' Answer Book*, I wish that I could join you and five or six other parents in a long talk about our adolescent sons and daughters. I believe we could learn from each other. We could compare notes, tell of question and answer sessions with our children which may have left us exhausted emotionally and physically, and admit to each other what we know and don't know about what is happening to us and to our youngsters in this terrifically sex-charged world. For, like it or not, we are living through a sexual explosion—and explosions always cause a fair amount of confusion. We are confused about what we should or should not tell our children and about what we should do or not do about the films, newspaper stories, magazine articles, books, and TV shows that assault our children's senses with sex and sexual love.

Since we can't talk over our groping efforts to understand our sexual selves and our sons and daughters, I am going to do the next best thing and write about what I've learned over the years about youngsters and their development. I hope I will answer many of your questions—and help you answer many of your children's questions. But I must warn you (and perhaps reassure you) that nothing that you merely *tell* your children about love and life will make as deep an impression as what they see for themselves in their own home. The children of parents who treat each other with affection, respect, and good humor learn the fundamental facts of love and life without a word being spoken. Naturally, beyond your warm and kindly example, you must at times also give them information—information about things they do not witness in everyday life at home. But even here it is less important to prove that you know all there is to know than it is to prove that you can speak *sensibly* about what you *do* know.

It isn't easy for most of us to enter into a conversation with our children about sex, reproduction, or childbirth. We're afraid that we'll run out of words in the middle, that we'll say "the wrong thing," that answering one question will raise others that may be even harder to get our tongues around. These anxieties are perfectly normal—and can usually be cured by a little practice with such conversations. A good person to practice with is your husband or wife. Perhaps another friendly parent can help you become accustomed to speaking openly and unselfconsciously about the facts of life. In saying out loud what we know and feel about sexual experience, love, family life, and childbearing, we find out not only how to use the words, but what these life-giving, terribly important human thoughts and actions really mean to us.

Over and over again parents have told me they knew what to say but could not find the right words. I hope the *Parents' Answer Book* will help you find these words.

I don't think that there ever has been a time when most parents spoke easily and calmly to their children about sex and reproduction. There may have been a few cold fish who rattled off the facts of life like a grocery list but they most likely did not know what they were talking about. When you are talking about men as men and women as women, romance, love, marriage, women having babies, the great joy and responsibility of rearing a family, your heart is *meant* to skip a beat. When we speak about something as powerful as life and love, it is not surprising that there are hesitations in our speech, bursts of excitement, barely audible whispers, rambling sentences that don't have a good beginning or end.

In the past, parents have not told their children much about sex and human reproduction. They have been shy to speak of the most fundamental of all life processes, the ability to reproduce. They also have wanted to shield their children from their own misconceptions, failures, disappointments. They have shied away from sharing an account of their sexual experiences and understandings. Twenty-five years ago a parent could still easily bypass sex education. He might have the nagging feeling he was somehow failing his child, but he could get some comfort from the fact

6

that sex and childbirth simply were not discussed in the open, that he was joining forces with millions of other silent parents. Parents are the child's first and most forceful teachers, but they have probably never been the primary source of plain sex education. Rather, it was from other children that children learned about sex. The story of human reproduction has been whispered in bits and pieces from one child to the next for generation after generation. Considering the secrecy which has enveloped the topics of sex and reproduction, it's a wonder that any youngster ever got the facts of life straight before experiencing them for himself.

When a parent remains silent about any critical area—reproduction, sex, death—his silence carries a message. The message may be "I don't know anything about that" or "I am angry with you for asking such a question" or "I am afraid to talk about that." And of course sometimes the message may be "I am listening; I understand." Let's examine these varieties of silence.

The silence of ignorance

Sometimes we do not speak because we simply do not know the answer. A child asks us an important question about sexual intercourse and we give an evasive answer because we do not have the facts. Some of us have been stumped when we were first asked, "Can a man put urine in his wife when they're having sexual intercourse?" The answer is, "No, there is a valve that automatically closes off the flow of urine." But we may have mumbled, "Of course not. Don't be silly." And our child persisted, "Why not? That's what a penis is for." And we said, "I don't know exactly why. Stop pestering me." Ignorance is no disgrace and should not drive you into silence, since there are always two things you *can* say: "I don't know the answer to that one," and "Let's see if we can find out."

Many of the simple factual questions that children frequently ask are answered in our *One Hundred Questions and Answers* at the end of this volume. We have studied hundreds of youngsters' questions and have written the most common ones in their language. You will not necessarily want to use the answers exactly as we have phrased them, but our answers are sound and you can confidently use them with your own wording. The *Life Cycle Library for Young People* can also be an invaluable aid for parents and children in their search for facts and knowledge about sexual development, sexual behavior, and human reproduction.

The silence of anger

When our children's questions shock us or catch us off guard, we sometimes cannot suppress an angry retort—"I don't want to hear you talking about things like that"—followed by a smoldering two-hour silence. The child, who may not even have known the meaning of the question, gets the message that some questions are dangerous to ask, and may conclude that it's safer not to ask any questions at all. Repetition of such episodes will eventually set a pattern of lifelong silence between parent and child on the subject of sex.

Our anger may spring from a number of different sources. We may be unhappy that our children have discovered something that we hoped to shield them from for a little longer. Or the question may have made us feel that we were neglecting the child's education in this area—and nothing hurts like the prick of a guilty conscience. Or the question may have touched an area that we simply do not want to think about, much less discuss with our children. Or we may have been reminded that our children are growing up and away from us, meeting people beyond our control, hearing and seeing things that we cannot censor.

All these reactions are normal—and understandable. And, usually, they seize us in an instant, before we have a chance to control them. But, after they've seized us—and after we've stomped off in a huff—we should try to spend the next minutes trying to cool down. It is human nature, I'm afraid, that we usually spend this time in convincing ourselves that we were *right* to be angry or in feeling guilty. It is far more useful to spend it trying to find the real source of the anger within ourselves. Once we find it, we then have to remind ourselves that, after all, we're only human—and all humans occasionally behave less than logically.

Having done this, we're ready for the awkward task of breaking silence. This need not be a big emotional production. It's enough to say, "I'm sorry I blew my cool a few minutes ago. Your question just caught me flat-footed. Would you mind giving it to me again?"

It isn't easy to admit to your child that you can sometimes be in the wrong; but if you can manage it, you're well on the way to winning his lifelong respect.

The silence of embarrassment

Our children's questions often embarrass us—and understandably so. What mother wants to tell her daughters about the physical and psychological miseries of her hysterectomy? What father wants the job of explaining grandpa's prostate operation? Who wants to face the task of explaining to his inquisitive ten-year-old the newspaper report of a rape? It is certainly hard going for parents to tell their own children about pain, evil, tragedy, and crime; but children need to hear about these matters from those they love and who love them. Trouble doesn't seem quite so bad when you hear about it in the shelter of your home and family. It's important not to keep silent about an inevitably miserable or painful experience, but you also do not have to go into it in minute detail.

Sometimes we don't tell children about frightening or unusual experiences of sex and reproduction because we think they are too young to understand. This most typically is not true.

We usually underestimate our children's readiness to understand simple, even ugly facts. And you'd be surprised what emotional relief they experience from the correct, undistorted facts.

Facts are usually much less frightening than what the youngsters have conjured up in their imaginations. Take one question which some of us have found difficult to answer: "Where does the baby come out when it's born?" There is certainly a temptation to bypass this with some vague answer like: "It comes out naturally from a special place in the mother." Now why do we feel we should hedge when asked about the vaginal opening and birth canal? First, the outlet of the birth canal is also a sexual organ and we become hesitant when we speak of this female center of sexual pleasure. Second, women associate the vagina with menstruation and dislike talking about the birth of the baby from this frequently blood-discharging orifice. Third, we find it hard to accept the fact that a full-sized baby can be pushed down and out of the vagina. We may know intellectually that the vagina is made to accommodate itself to the birth of a baby; but emotionally we may be a bit wary of the idea.

If you don't state exactly how a baby is delivered, you may be sure the youngster will conclude from your silence that the truth is too horrible to speak and will proceed to dream up the most weird and hurtful fantasies. One young boy was positive that every woman had a zipper from her belly button to her pubic bone and worried that the zipper might get stuck. A teenage girl was sure the baby popped out from the mother's belly button and had nightmares of her mother's belly being burst open by the new baby.

A calm and gentle explanation of how the vagina stretches and the baby is pushed out of the opening between the urethra and anus is far better than the gory, inaccurate myths. If the youngster is not emotionally ready to assimilate some fact it will usually go in one ear and out the other. Most children have an excellent protective forgetting device.

For the most part, it is our own unpreparedness for awkward questions that causes us embarrassment. Since we secretly hope that our child will not ask us about masturbation or sodomy or rape, we never ask ourselves how we *would* answer him. Parents can spare themselves a great deal of embarrassment by finding the right words in advance. And the practice this gives them will make it much more comfortable for them to answer the questions that they have *not* foreseen.

The silence of understanding

A growing child needs many listening hours from his parents. These are times when we just sit and let them speak their minds fully and naturally, without feeling under pressure to instruct them or to justify ourselves or to defend a world that may seem baffling and hostile to our children.

This form of silence, unlike the others, is hard for us to maintain. We find it difficult to be good listeners to our children. It hurts to know that we have been unable to shield them from the same growing-up pains that we suffered as adolescents. It hurts to know that there is no way to convince them that matters that overwhelm them today will be forgotten in a few years.

But, in the end, we can only listen respectfully and sympathetically. If we try to assure them that their difficulties are not really serious or that they will resolve themselves in time, our children simply conclude that we "just don't understand." And in a sense they're right: we can no more experience their adolescent anxieties than they can experience our adult assurance.

Listening is perhaps the hardest art we parents can learn. Yet, as the years pass and our children come back to us again and again because they know they will be listened to, it will prove to have been worth the effort.

The goals of sex education

In thinking about the welfare and happiness of our children, we naturally wonder about our goals in sex education. I believe most of us would agree our primary teaching goals are not sexual and reproductive body mechanics, not tried and true tricks of capturing and holding a mate, not just the achievement of sexual happiness and pleasure. None of these is to be sniffed at or crossed off our list of desired outcomes, but we have higher goals. A thoughtful and compassionate statement of what our goals in sex education should be has been offered by Dr. Warren Johnson in his book *Human Sex and Sex Education* (Philadelphia: Lea and Febiger, 1963, p. 193). There he addressed himself primarily to educators. I have recast his statement for parents: Parents are wise sex educators when they help young people:

    to be more involved *with* people than *against* people;

    to be capable of giving respect and not just winning it;

    to be more loving than lovely;

    to be capable of friendship and not just friendliness;

    to be more prone to accept themselves, physically and mentally, than to reject;

    to be free of a sense of obligation to tell other people, including future mates and children, how they should live.

This is basic sex education.

2

What Is
Normal Development?

Many children worry, "Am I normal?" So many rapid changes happen during adolescence that boys and girls often wonder if they are changing in a normal way. And parents worry, too. We live in a very competitive society and even compete with our neighbors about our children's growth. We notice that our neighbors' girl is still flat-chested while our daughter has bought her first bra. We also notice that their 16-year-old son is six feet tall, while ours seems to have been five feet three for years.

To see our children grow well, become big and strong, briskly step into maturity makes us feel good. We have a tendency to push youngsters into looking and behaving like adults too early. In the early years of adolescence, from ten to 15, most youngsters would just as soon take it easy as far as becoming adults is concerned. In the beginning of the teen years, adolescents tend to be shy, rather cautious, and tentative about their first approaches to boy-girl relationships.

This first shyness does not usually last long and parents would do well to respect it and not force young people into social relationships in which they feel ill at ease and clumsy.

Average or normal?

People often confuse *average* with *normal,* but the two are entirely different and are arrived at in entirely different ways. If you wanted to find the *average* driving time to a town 30 miles away, you might keep a daily record over a year. You would then add the times—including the occasions when you were delayed by a

flat tire, by a truck overturned on the road, by a vapor-locked engine—and divide by the number of trips. This would give you a single value, say 46 minutes, as an average.

If you wanted to find the *normal* driving time, you would exclude the trips that involved the flat tire, the overturned truck, and the vapor-locked engine, and concentrate only on the ordinary trips. You would find that your fastest trip was, say, 34 minutes, your slowest 45 minutes. Any driving time within this range would be considered *normal*.

This is the way your doctor thinks about normalcy—not in terms of an average, but in terms of a normal range. When he says that girls *normally* begin to menstruate between the ages of nine and 15, he means that youngsters he has encountered began to menstruate within this range.

Most young people are not aware of the fantastically wide range of perfectly normal human characteristics or behaviors. Take, for example, the onset of puberty. Boys normally become sexually mature between ages 11 and 18, and girls between ages nine and 15—a span of seven or eight years, at least one-half of the childhood years.

Another example is bust size. The manufacturers of brassieres know very well that women go from size 30, AA cup to C cup, up to size 44, B cup to EE cup. And if you can't find your exact fit within this wide array, there are still other accommodations that can be made. What applies to the female bosom applies to practically every part of the human anatomy: feet, noses, chins, heights, weights, and last, but certainly not least, sexual organs.

The normal human being comes in all shapes and sizes, and there is an infinite variety of ways he can lead a productive, happy, satisfying, and satisfactory life. Some parents and their children are handicapped by a lack of imagination and daring. Short men have become movie stars, flat-chested women have become high fashion models, girls who never had a date until they were 17 have married well and happily, boys who were famous for their sexual escapades before they married have settled down to be ideal husbands and fathers.

The fact of the matter is that there is almost no way to predict how anybody's life is going to develop within the surprisingly wide normal range of growth and development.

Variety within the normal range

If there are broad variations in sexual development among children of the *same* age and sex, there are even broader variations among children of *different* ages and sexes. For example, a nine-year-old girl might reach sexual maturity before her 16-year-old brother does. Some experts have suggested we should abandon grouping children by chronological age altogether, since it frequently has so little to do with physical or psychological maturity.

During the sixth, seventh and eighth grades you have a most uncomfortable and awkward situation. Half the girls in sixth grade have reached puberty and almost 90 percent have done so by the end of seventh grade. On the other hand, only a small fraction of seventh-grade boys have reached puberty—ten percent or so. A girl's initiation into womanhood includes her being exasperated by most of the boys in her class because they are such shrimps. She spends a fair amount of time mooning over a possible glance or quick hello from a ninth-grade boy who has finally become a man. The average seventh-grade boy, on the other hand, looks at the towering amazons around him, or the short young women with nicely developed breasts, and wonders how anyone could ever imagine him falling in love with these creatures. Certainly the battle of the sexes gets a good send-off in the adolescent disequilibrium between boys and girls of the same chronological age.

There is yet another source of normal differences between adolescent boys and girls. Girls mature sexually sooner than boys, but their development of sexual desires is more gradual. Many young women do not become fully sexually alive until they are married and well into their twenties or even thirties. Young men, on the other hand, become sexually mature later, but almost immediately reach their peak of sexual desire. By the age of 15 about 90 percent of boys have experienced orgasm from some source, whereas less than one-third of the girls have done so.

This difference between girls and boys in their responsiveness and search for sexual outlets should be borne in mind by both parents and their teenage youngsters. A girl may look deliciously seductive and yet not feel any great urgency to engage in much intimate sexual activity. The young woman may not realize that her lovely curved form and her every move send her date into spasms of real and imagined ecstasies. This is not to say that adolescent girls have no sexual feelings; they most certainly do. But these throbs and wonderful sensations do not usually come into full bloom until the young woman is close to her twentieth birthday. This slower development of a woman's sexual feelings suggests that it may have to be the girl who sets the limits on necking and petting, because she is usually not quite as much under the spell of her sexual drives. The point here is that it is perfectly normal for a young man to be extremely eager for sexual experiences and therefore to need a young woman's help in keeping his desires within sensible bounds.

The variety and range of sexual roles

Times most certainly have changed since World War I. Women have not only won the right to vote but have greatly increased the variety and range of activities they may participate in without being ostracized by the community. Along with a greater choice of occupation, women have achieved greater comfort with their wish to be competent, strong, and steady, and much freer in their expression of sexual feelings. We have seen the gradual disintegration of the Victorian myth that women are meant to be frail and fearful creatures, a bit weak in the head, and easily moved by high ideals and romatic notions (but never, heaven forbid, by plain sexual desire).

Similarly, masculinity is not as narrowly defined as it once was. We are realizing that, just as men do not hold exclusive rights to such virtues as competence, courage, and ambition, so women do not hold exclusive rights to such virtues as tenderness, sensitivity, and compassion. We have also come to a point where men can try their hands at almost every occupation usually thought of as being feminine without being laughed at. I once gave a lecture in a very staid, traditional women's club on the changing social roles of men and women today. It was during the 1968 Presidential campaign, and I told the group that Senator Edmund Muskie might get my vote for vice-president because I had heard on a news broadcast that he had made the drapes for their Washington home. A woman immediately rose to her feet and asked for the floor. She reported that one of their older members, a Mrs. Roberts, had recently retired from the club and moved to the country. In recognition of her work, the club had decided to take her an azalea plant. The speaker arrived at the house with the plant but could not find Mrs. Roberts. She followed the sound of a sewing machine to the dining room and found *Mr.* Roberts busily working on a new set of drapes for the living room. Mr. Roberts then directed the speaker to the patio, where she found the sixty-five-year-old *Mrs.* Roberts dressed in an old shirt and slacks on her hands and knees laying a brick floor. Over coffee, Mrs. Roberts explained: "We like trying what the other one has been doing. It keeps you on your toes."

It should be noted that such easy exchanges of activities by men and women usually indicates that they are very secure in their own masculinity or femininity. A young man or woman must be pretty sure of himself or herself as a male or female before venturing away from safe and conventional sex roles. It is only gradually, as experience and confidence grows, that a person may dare to develop all of his or her potential and become a truly unique individual.

The quest for individuality

All of us want to be normal, because normalcy usually means good health and sound development. At the same time, we do not want to be exactly like everyone else; we want to be individuals. This conflict between normalcy and individuality is especially keen during the adolescent years. Youngsters are miserable if they think they are not normal, but they'd rather die than be considered ordinary. Sometimes the worst thing a parent can say to his growing teenager is that there is nothing unusual about his development or that his trials and tribulations have been lived

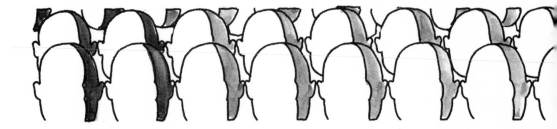

through by every human being on the face of the earth. When a youngster suffers, he is convinced that no one has ever felt quite that way before, and when he is flying high he's just as sure he's the only one who has felt such utter joy. There are times when the parent can do little beyond offering reassurance for his anxieties, sympathy for his sorrows, and enthusiastic congratulations for his triumphs. He will learn soon enough, without our telling him, that there are anxieties, sorrows, and triumphs far beyond the adolescent's imagination.

We are often exasperated because our youngsters, in their quest for individuality, work so hard at being different—in exactly the same way all their friends are "being different." They adopt weird clothes, outlandish tricks of makeup, or bizarre hair styles —all very "different" and all pretty much alike. This behavior is not as frivolous as it seems. It serves to announce to parents and to the adult world at large that the adolescent is determined to win adult status—to be independent of the parental tastes and judgments that dominated his childhood. But, while the adolescent yearns for adult independence, he is also frightened by it, and so wants plenty of company—friends and classmates who will take the same risks he is taking. When your son refuses to have his hair cut because "all the guys are wearing it this way," he really means, "If I give in on this, everyone will know I've fallen back to childhood status."

It is probable that some of the dynamism of our culture results from the fact that our adolescents feel they must overturn the older generation in order to win adulthood for themselves. In primitive cultures, adulthood is automatically conferred upon adolescents when they reach a certain age and have passed through traditional puberty rites. Such cultures undoubtedly have more peaceable homes—but they do not put a premium on initiative, experimentation, and aggressive pursuit of progress.

Throughout the *Life Cycle Library for Young People* we have drawn in broad strokes our common humanity, the developments which every boy and girl must pass through as they approach adulthood. But we also have laid great emphasis on each youngster's unique individuality. It is simply a fact that there is only one person in the world exactly like your son or daughter. Each person is endowed with his own particular inherited characteristics and grows up in his own very special environment. It is by developing the full potential given him by his inheritance and environment that one acquires individuality. One of our hopes is that each generation will be better able to accept and revel in the wide differences between human beings, each with his own tastes, talents, and ambitions. The rich potential and enormous variety of the human condition is surely one of our greatest reasons to hope for survival.

3

How Your Son
Becomes a Man

Boys become sexually mature during the teen years, usually by the age of 18. This period of transition from childhood to manhood is called adolescence. By sexually mature we mean "able to reproduce." When a boy reaches the point at which he is able to reproduce, we say that he has reached puberty. Many people guess at a boy's sexual maturity by the growth of hair on his face or by his height. A beard is a good external sign of sexual maturity, and you can be practically positive that a six-footer is sexually mature. On the other hand, a young man who is short and has very little facial hair may be sexually mature.

Variations in the onset and pace of adolescent development can be sources of concern to parents and their boys. For some boys, adolescent changes begin early. For other boys just as normal, these changes may begin much later. The most comforting comment that can be made is that all children do finally live through adolescence and the differences between boys level off.

Although we cannot tell a boy exactly when he may expect adolescent physical changes to begin or how long it will take to go through the series, we can tell him the order in which they will appear. The sequence is as follows: beginning growth of testes and penis, first pubic hair (straight, pigmented), early voice changes first ejaculation and nocturnal emissions, kinky pubic hair, growth spurt, underarm hair, marked voice changes, and development of the beard. These developments overlap, and the full series takes about five years.

About ten percent of boys have reached puberty by the time they are 11 years old and fewer than ten percent reach it after the age of 16. On the average, boys reach puberty at about 14½. It is all very well for us to speak calmly of averages. Six months one way or another doesn't seem very much to us, but for a boy who is anxiously waiting for adolescent changes to begin, each month can seem like a year. Watching his age-mates get tall and begin to wear athletic supporters for gym, a junior high school boy may well begin to think something is wrong with his pace of growth.

Here a father's own experience may be helpful. He may be able to describe a late and sudden growth spurt that he or one of his friends went through. Concrete details of actual experiences are reassuring.

The endocrine system

The changes that occur at the age of puberty and throughout adolescence begin with the pituitary gland, a gland no larger than a pea, located below the brain and deep within the head. The pituitary gland is part of a body system called the endocrine system. Most body systems are series of connected organs, like the digestive system or the nervous system. But the endocrine system is made up of glands that are not connected to each other, even though they have one special function in common. The special function of the endocrine glands is the secretion of hormones (chemical substances) into the bloodstream. It is because of the interrelationship of the endocrine glands and their hormones that they are referred to as a "system."

The major glands that make up the endocrine system are the pituitary, thyroid, parathyroid, adrenal, and sex glands. The sex glands are called gonads. The gonads in a boy are the testicles; in a girl they are the ovaries.

The hormones produced by the endocrine glands regulate many functions of the body. It is a chain reaction among the endocrine glands, beginning at puberty, that produces the adolescent changes. At puberty the pituitary gland secretes a hormone that causes the testicles to begin producing sperm cells and male hormones, called androgens. These androgens—the most important of which is testosterone—cause other physical changes in the body, such as the secondary sex characteristics.

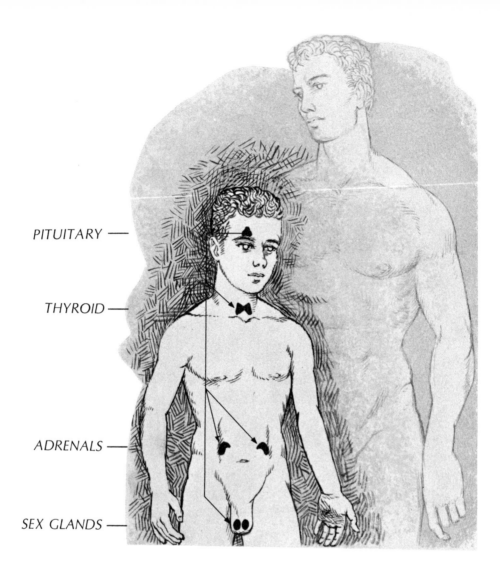

PITUITARY —

THYROID —

ADRENALS —

SEX GLANDS —

Every human being has hormones of both sexes. A boy will have a small amount of female hormones (estrogens), and a girl will have a small amount of male hormones. This is quite normal.

What causes the pituitary gland to release its hormone is still not fully known. Many scientists believe that it is triggered by the hypothalamus, a minute part of the brain that plays an important role in the regulation of bodily functions. The timing of this signal, however, varies among boys, and is believed to be at least partly based on hereditary factors.

Very rarely, a boy's sexual development may not take place normally because of a malfunctioning of his endocrine system. If this does occur, it can usually be corrected by medical treatment.

The endocrine system is a very complicated system of glandular checks and balances and only a doctor skilled in the treatment of the endocrine malfunction should be consulted. There is usually no glandular basis for homosexuality.

Growth of the sex organs

Usually the first sign of puberty in a boy is the growth of his sex organs. The male sex organs are the testicles (or testes) and the penis. They are the external organs of the male reproductive system, a complex body system that is responsible for producing sperm, storing them, and depositing them in the body of a female. The penis is external because it must enter the vagina of the female to deposit the sperm. The testicles are external because sperm cannot be produced at the slightly higher temperatures that exist inside the body.

At puberty the testicles grow to about an inch in diameter. One will normally hang lower than the other. The penis will also grow and develop along with the testicles. Sex organs will vary in size among boys just as hands and feet do.

Boys can be spared needless worry if some of the myths about penis size can be replaced by facts. *Myth: Penis size tells you how much a "man" you are, how virile and fertile you are.* Fact: Penises come in all sizes, and there is no truth in the old idea that boys or men with large penises are any more sexually potent or powerful

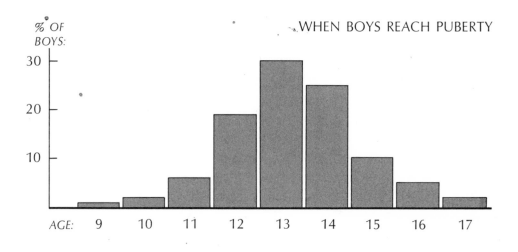

24

than those with small ones. *Myth: You can guess the size of a man's penis from the size of his hands or feet.* Fact: Penis size is independent of other body parts or overall height. *Myth: A woman prefers to have sexual intercourse with a man with a large penis.* Fact: The size of a penis makes no difference in the amount of sexual pleasure it can give, or in a man's ability to perform sexually; women say that love, tenderness, thoughtfulness are far more important than penis size. *Myth: Masturbation can permanently change the shape and size of your penis and testicles.* Fact: The penis enlarges during an erection and after the erection has passed —or after ejaculation—it returns to its original size.

A boy's voice gradually becomes deeper throughout adolescence. Here again we have great variability, one boy going smoothly from soprano to bass, another suffering with a voice that always seems to break at the most embarrassing times.

The next sign of sexual maturity is first ejaculation. Some boys have their first ejaculation as early as nine, others not until they are 17. By far the most common cause of these ejaculations is masturbation. Most adults are confused about what they should think and feel about masturbation. Most of us were brought up to believe that masturbation is in some way harmful. We felt guilty when we masturbated and we sought ways to overcome what seemed at best to be a nasty habit. Today, however, physicians, psychiatrists, psychologists, and scientists who study sexual behavior assure us that masturbation is not only harmless but an almost universal practice. What can cause trouble is for a person to unmercifully blame himself for doing something which is normal and enjoyable. The sense of guilt and shame are the culprits, not the masturbation. Is masturbation sometimes a sign that a child or adult is unhappy? Of course it is. We think of eating, handwashing, and house-cleaning as thoroughly normal actions, yet even these, when performed compulsively, may be signals of distress.

If distress is the cause of compulsive behavior, we should try to relieve the distress and leave the behavior alone, whether it's eating, handwashing, house-cleaning, or masturbation. Attacking such behavior, which is simply a symptom, not a cause, merely gives the individual a new cause for distress. In the case of masturbation, censure or outright prohibition will probably increase the youngster's need for this form of sexual release.

Excess semen is often given off at night while a boy is sleeping. Boys should be prepared for these nocturnal emissions; to wake up in the morning with wet pajamas and not know how they got wet can be very embarrassing. "Wet dreams" are completely normal, simply nature's way of ridding the body of the semen that it can no longer store. Their frequency will vary from one boy to another. It is also perfectly normal for a boy never to have a wet dream. A boy may wake up in the middle of a wet dream or he may sleep through and not notice the emission until morning.

Parents sometimes have to break old habits to accommodate the exaggerated modesty adolescents often feel. Mothers in particular are used to sticking their heads into the bathroom when their children are bathing or barging into bedrooms when youngsters are getting dressed. Mothers also may feel they are doing a youngster a good turn by straightening up his dresser drawers or closet. The absolute rule about adolescent property should be: Private Property—Keep Out, And This Means You.

The adolescent growth spurt

The most visible change during adolescence is the teenage youngster's attainment of adult height and body build. As developments go in childhood, this one happens fast. A mother will be buying size 12 clothes for her son while he is ten, 11, and 12 years old, and suddenly her youngster is into size 16. The spurt in height may begin as early as age 11 and as late as age 16. There are several differences between boys who have their growth spurt early and those who have it late. The early maturers are more likely to be big for their age when they are in elementary school; the growth spurt begins for them suddenly and is of relatively short duration. They literally become young men overnight. For a year or so the early maturing boy will be much larger than his friends and he may *look* a great deal more grown up than he feels. Parents may expect too much heavy work and adult behavior from these young men because they look physically stronger than they actually are.

The late maturing boy may spend a good deal of time worrying whether he will ever catch up with his friends. An important fact to determine is whether he has already experienced an accelerated period of growth, say four or more inches in one year.

26

If he has not, you can assure him that his present shortness is temporary and that, whatever his current height is, he will probably grow another six inches or more. He will go through a longer period of slow, preadolescent growth than his early-maturing friends and so may actually end up taller than his age-mates. The late maturing boy may also be teased by his friends for being chubby. Again he needs reassurance that his day will come and that boys who mature late are likely to have a long, lean body build. Boys who mature early are more likely to be large, stocky, and broad-shouldered. It has always been my guess that Spencer Tracy was an early developer and Gary Cooper a late developer.

The last changes

The last adolescent growth changes for the boy are the development of a beard and the final lowering of his voice. It is amazing how violent adults and young people can get about hair. Long hair, or any exotic hair style for that matter, and a scraggly or gloriously full beard are tremendously effective in stirring up a fight between parents and their son. I would caution parents to take it easy in their reaction to any hair style, short, long, curly, or straight. You can shear off a great deal of a person's feelings of importance and individuality by shearing off his hair. A prison haircut, down to the scalp, is designed to do just this. The youngster will cling to his hair style as if his manhood were at stake, and a parental challenge will more than likely only increase his determination to hold fast.

I doubt very much that hair styles and beards are worth more than a minute's discussion, and then only when the hair is hopelessly dirty. We should remind ourselves that hair styles come and go, and crew cuts may be back with us in another ten years.

Masculine identity

From the moment of his birth, when his father and mother first see that he is equipped with a penis and testicles, a young boy is guided into his role as man-child. He is given a boy's name, his father is congratulated for having conceived a son, his mother may find herself quietly beaming to find herself with yet another man to love, friends may contribute a tiny baseball mit or boxing gloves to dangle in his crib. From birth on, the baby with male genitals is subtly and almost forcibly educated to *act* like a boy.

When our boy baby grows into a school-age child, he is expected not only to behave like a boy, but to begin to learn the many skills that he will need in his work as a man. For some boys these years are filled with excitement and challenge. For others, who may be just as bright, this can be a period of defeat and boredom. Elementary teachers are for the most part women, and the world they create around them tends to be a feminine world, orderly, neat, clean, and quiet—not the sort of world most boys prefer. As a result, elementary school boys may fight the system out of frustration and boredom. Boys who will not join in this male rebellion are "teacher's pets," held in contempt even by most of the girls. During the last years of elementary school the boy will hold to his cluster of boy friends with a terrific tenacity. It is as if, by a single look at a girl, he might be swallowed up by the world of women. If he does glance at a girl, you can be sure he is safely surrounded by a pack of boys. Little by little he becomes more daring, and by junior high school most boys are willing to admit that girls may occasionally be nice to have around.

While a boy is a baby, a toddler, and a school-age child, he is constantly involved with some aspect of his sexual being. Sex and love do not come zooming in out of the blue during adolescence. A boy has loved and been loved by his parents. He has probably thought that his mother was the most beautiful woman in the world and that someday he would steal her from his father. He marveled at and wondered about his father's love for his mother, and probably reasoned that anyone his father loved that much must be the only one for him. In addition to being loved and loving in return, the young boy has had experience with plain sex. His lips have a delicious sensitivity developed in part from sucking at his mother's breast or from a bottle during infancy. He has enjoyed the sensual pleasure of a warm bath, a cozy quilt or blanket on a cold night, the exhilaration of moving his body in strenuous exercise. He has also handled his penis thousands of times to urinate and from time to time to masturbate. He may have worried whether he could somehow be deprived of this most essential organ.

In adolescence, the transient, sporadic, gentle interests in sex suddenly surge into high gear. During this peak of his sexual desires and activities, in the years from 16 to 20, he may masturbate three or more times a week, pet to orgasm with his date, and, if married, have sexual intercourse more frequently than during any later period. And during this peak period, it is inevitable that he will live under great pressure and perhaps in severe conflict. Our films, our advertising, our books, our feminine fashions seem designed to keep him perpetually drooling with desire and simmering with fantasies of sexual adventure. Parents, teachers, and clergy face a difficult task in trying to persuade him, against his overheated inclinations, that the casual, raw sex of the fantasies is in real life impersonal, unsatisfying, dehumanizing, and in the end, an ugly bore.

Because we are adults—because we've had time to digest a few decades of adult experience—we know that having sex without love, humor, patience, gentleness, and thoughtfulness is like having a picnic without fresh air, sun, grass, and trees. As adults we've had time to see what sex is—and isn't—and have learned how to weave our plain sexual urges into the fabric of our lives. We know that raw sex may be the basic fuel of life, but we also know that it must be fed judiciously into the motor of human experience— sometimes lavishly, sometimes sparingly. And, because our children are still children, they have not had time to acquire either our adult experience or our adult viewpoint. Balance, moderation, perspective, and judiciousness are simply not the characteristics of youth. While living with a young man who has just become sexually strong and active, we should try to remind ourselves that, although he has been preparing for this change throughout his childhood and adolescence, it comes swiftly and forcefully and may put him off balance for a time. It will inevitably be a number of years before he learns how to live comfortably with his newly-awakened sexuality.

4

How Your Daughter
Becomes a Woman

Every woman knows there is a great deal more to becoming a woman than developing breasts and beginning to menstruate; but, in the early years of a girl's adolescent development, these may seem to her to be most important physical steps toward womanhood. The glandular changes that take place during adolescence are basically the same for boys and girls. A full description of these changes and their effects is given on page 22.

Briefly, maturation in a girl is a chain reaction begun by the pituitary gland, which secretes a hormone that causes her sex glands, the ovaries, to mature. The ovaries, in turn, secrete hormones that cause overall physical growth, maturation of her reproductive organs, and development of the secondary sex characteristics that make her begin to look like a woman.

Breasts come first

The first visible sign that a girl is becoming a woman is the growth of her breasts, beginning several years before first menstruation. It is wise to keep track of your daughter's breast development, because it will remind you to prepare her for her first menstrual period if you have not already done so. Each girl has her own timetable of breast development, but the general order of changes is the same. First, the nipples grow out a bit and the dark circles around them puff up. Then the breasts expand, pushing out into cone-shapes and gradually into fuller, hemispherical shapes.

Visitors to our country have the impression that we are quite bosom-mad. We have made a woman's breasts not only her most visible but also her most potent sexual attraction. In some lands beautifully shaped buttocks and a sinuous gait are the key points of a woman's sexual beauty. In our glorification of the female breast as a sexual attraction, we tend to lose track of its basic purpose, which is to suckle babies, supplying both sustenance and the feeling of being loved. Growing girls should be told why women have breasts and why doctors and psychologists advise breast feeding, if only for the first weeks or months of the new baby's life. The most obvious reason is that the mother's own milk is the best food her baby can have; no laboratory has succeeded or is likely to succeed in improving on it. The mother's milk also contains a unique substance called colostrum, which serves to protect the infant from infection. In addition to being a very pleasurable sensation for the mother, nursing also serves to bring her uterus back to its original size. And, perhaps most important of all, the breast-fed baby is likely to be happier, more responsive, and more secure than the baby deprived of this luscious physical experience —and is likely to carry these advantages into later life.

It is a silly myth that men universally admire women with giant breasts, just as it is a silly myth that women universally admire men with giant muscles. Many very beautiful and sexually glamorous women have very small breasts indeed. Slight or modest breasts can be as fascinating and appealing as large breasts. A growing girl can be embarrassed by her sudden development of

good-sized breasts. She will need her mother's help in selecting a well-fitted brassiere, one that will give her excellent support and increase her sense of poise. She will also need her mother's help in picking clothes which set off her new womanly figure. With small breasts or large, the key to a girl's good looks is posture. A girl standing erect and proud of her body, whatever its dimensions, is a beautiful sight.

Breast development is usually accompanied by the development of pubic hair and of hair under the arms and on the legs.

The growth spurt

A girl may begin her growth spurt as early as 10 years of age or as late as 16. The most rapid increase in height usually occurs a couple of years before she begins to menstruate. The early maturing girl may feel very awkward as she develops womanly characteristics while her friends remain flat-chested tomboys. For a while, she may tower over everyone in her class, both girls and boys, but when the other children catch up to her she may be only moderately tall or even short in comparison. Since the late maturing girl's adolescent growth spurt comes on top of a long preadolescent period of growth, she may become a fairly tall young woman. Fortunately, now that fashion designers have discovered the beauty of tall, willowy women, young girls no longer have any reason to hide their height by slumping or to feel miserable over their long legs.

Menstruation

To a young girl about to be a teenager, the menarche—the first menstruation—is a most significant event. With her first menstruation, she leaves childhood and enters the world of women. Life will never be quite the same.

Menstruation is a normal function of the female body, but it provokes many worries and fears in youngsters. Boys as well as girls should understand menstruation, because an adolescent girl deserves the understanding not only of other women but also of men about this intimate process. I once overheard the following exchange between a mother and her adolescent daughter:

Daughter: Mom, I've just begun my period. I want to go with the kids on a picnic. Where can I carry some extra sanitary pads?

Mother: That's easy. Wrap them in some tissue and put them in your purse.

Daughter: But what if a boy gets my purse and opens it? That would be awful. He'd know.

Mother: Don't be a worry-wart. First of all let's hope he's got enough sense not to open a woman's pocketbook. A woman's purse is private property. Second, if he does, it won't matter because he'll understand. Today menstruation isn't a secret to boys.

It is amazing that, generation after generation, the crazy notion that menstruation is some kind of sickness persists. Not only a sickness but a poisonous affliction. Only 15 years ago, while teaching a college course in adolescent psychology, I found that a number of my students still believed that a menstruating woman could make a flower wilt by touching it. Many persons still think that women can not manage careers, because once a month they are nervous and irresponsible. With today's sensible health rules, the vast majority of women experience menstruation without any physical or psychological trouble.

A girl's attitude toward menstruation may reflect her more general feelings about being a woman. Her mother's happy acceptance

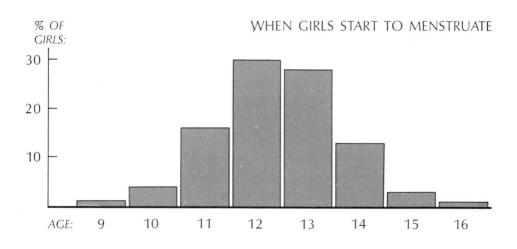

% OF GIRLS:

WHEN GIRLS START TO MENSTRUATE

AGE: 9 10 11 12 13 14 15 16

of womanhood is usually very important in the girl's acceptance of feminine functions and behaviors. At the same time, it makes little sense to become romantic when talking about menstruation to the practical adolescents of the 1970s. Girls told that menstruation is the beautiful, almost sanctified sign that they have joined the company of sexually mature women can sensibly ask: "What's so great about bleeding once a month?" Menstruation, while hardly a blessing, is not a cross either. Now that we have convenient and efficient methods of sanitary protection, it can perhaps be described best as a nuisance. It is easier for the young woman to accept menstruation if she knows some facts about it.

Facts about menstruation

The menstrual period is actually only one part of the entire menstrual cycle. The menstrual cycle is also called the reproductive cycle, because it is the continual preparation of woman's body to reproduce another human being.

When a girl is born, her ovaries contain about 400,000 eggs, all that she will have in her life. In fact, only about 400 of these eggs will ever be released from her ovaries. No one can explain why the ovaries contain thousands of eggs when only 400 are released.

Each month the pituitary gland sends out hormones that are carried through the bloodstream to the ovaries, causing one of them to begin ripening an egg. The ripened egg may be produced by either ovary. The ovaries usually ripen eggs in alternate months.

As the egg in the ovary ripens, the uterus lining thickens and stores up blood. This thickened lining is meant to serve as a bed for the fertilized egg. It is built up each cycle whether or not the egg is fertilized.

After an egg has ripened, it is released from the ovary. This is called ovulation. Ovulation occurs halfway through the 28-day menstrual cycle. This halfway point is about 14 days after the beginning of the previous menstrual period.

Most girls and women never know when they are ovulating. A few feel a side-ache or slight twinge or have a small amount of vaginal bleeding when the ripened egg is released from the ovary. After the egg leaves the ovary, it is caught by the Fallopian tube nearest it. The egg floats down this tube toward the uterus—it cannot propel itself like a sperm. Once in the tube, the egg can be fertilized by a sperm cell from a male.

If the egg is fertilized, it continues down to the uterus and lodges itself in the lining.

If the egg is not fertilized, it shrivels up and continues down the Fallopian tube, a trip that takes several days. The enriched lining of the uterus is not needed if the egg is not fertilized. It begins to shrink, and is shed from the uterus through the vagina. The unfertilized egg leaves the body with the lining.

The amount of menstrual flow, the number of days of flow, and the number of days between periods vary greatly from woman to woman. What is normal for one may be quite unusual for another.

When a girl begins to menstruate, her periods may be irregular. One time the flow may be quite heavy and last for over a week. At the next period, the flow may be light for only a few days. All these variations are normal, because the hormone secretion which regulates the menstrual cycle takes time to become regular. Each girl eventually settles down to her own pattern. Even then, it is normal and usual for her pattern to vary occasionally. Emotional upset, fatigue, or anxiety can change the timing or amount of discharge.

On the average, the menstrual period occurs every 28 days. But girls with cycles of 20 days or 35 days are within the normal range. Every girl should remember that her period is likely to be changeable in the beginning, and that it is not unusual to skip a month while the menstrual cycle is being established.

When a girl begins to menstruate, the pituitary hormone is usually too weak to stimulate the ovary to release an egg. But as this hormone repeats its signal each cycle, the signal becomes stronger and eventually stimulates the ovary to release a ripened egg. A girl may begin ovulating anywhere from a few months to a year after her first menstruation. Meanwhile, the lining of the uterus is built up each cycle in preparation for an egg. So a girl may have a periodic menstrual discharge even though she is not yet ovulating.

The normal range for the beginning of menstruation is quite wide—age nine to age 16, the commonest ages being 11 and 12. A girl who begins menstruating at 14 is just as normal and just as feminine as a girl who starts at 11. Ironically, girls who begin menstruating early usually menstruate to an older age than girls who begin late. Women stop menstruating in their forties or early fifties. Again, there is no exact time or best time for this to happen. The time when a woman stops menstruating is called her menopause or climacteric. She cannot conceive after the menopause.

Menstrual protection

When a girl begins to grow tall and to develop breasts, she should be prepared for her first menstrual period, which probably will occur during the next year or so. Manufacturers of sanitary pads and tampons have attractive introductory package for teenagers. Girls often worry about having an "accident" or about odor when they are menstruating. Sanitary pads come in several thicknesses and sizes, and a girl can use the size best suited to her amount of flow. Most youngsters overestimate amount of menstrual flow; the total average flow is half a cup. During the first two days of the period, when about half of the total amount is discharged, protection should be changed frequently. Less bulky pads or tampons can be used when the flow diminishes.

Menstrual blood by itself has no odor. The odor only occurs when the blood comes in contact with air. When the flow collects on a sanitary pad, it is exposed to the air, and the warmth of the body increases the odor. That is why pads are changed frequently or are dusted with a deodorant powder. Many girls prefer tampons. Since these are worn internally, where no air is present, no odor forms. The hymenal opening is normally large enough to permit the insertion of a tampon.

Myths about menstruation

Menstruation, like the penis, generates many myths, and you can help your daughter by replacing them with facts.

Myth: Loss of menstrual blood is weakening. Fact: The menstrual flow consists of tissue, watery fluids, and only a small amount of blood; even if it were entirely blood, the flow—usually no more than half a cup—would be insufficient to cause any weakness.

Myth: Menstruation lowers your resistance and makes you more susceptible to catching cold. Fact: There is no relationship between menstruation and catching a cold or any other illness.

Myth: A boy can tell by looking at a girl that she is having her period. Fact: There are no outward physical signs of menstruation.

Myth: Menstrual flow will stop if you take a bath. Fact: Warm (not hot) baths are not only safe but essential to comfort. If a girl prefers showers, even cold ones, there is no reason to skip them.

The feminine identity

Although a girl does not reach reproductive maturity until adolescence, she has been preparing for her adult role all her life. Her chief model, her mother, has been constantly in view, showing her how to become a woman, a wife, a mother, a homemaker. Her teachers, most of them women, and the mothers of her friends have shown her dozens of variations on the theme of womanhood. It is no wonder that girls come into adolescence with greater assurance than do boys, who rarely see a man before dinner-time. And because her mother's role in reproduction is more evident than her father's, it is likely that she will have a clearer anticipation of what sexual adulthood will mean to her. She has felt her body and discovered its sensitive spots. She may have masturbated and gotten some idea of what sexual excitement is all about.

The most obvious purpose of a young woman's sexual or, more correctly, reproductive maturation is that it enables her to have a baby. Today, in our eagerness to understand the *experience* of sex, we sometimes underplay the *function* of sex—the creation of new human life. In the *Life Cycle Library for Young People* we tell a great deal about how a baby is created, develops prenatally, is cared for as a newborn, and develops during childhood. We believe that young people should have solid information about the joys and problems, challenges and responsibilities of becoming parents. Early in life, young people need to think of themselves not only as happy, freely loving individuals but also as husbands and wives who may become parents. The full maturation of a girl's reproductive system offers her the promise of some day having a baby. Today, this is far from the only major experience in her life, but it inevitably influences all her mature life experiences.

A fundamental change has taken place in our society over the past century: a woman is more than a mother. Until this century a girl's central purpose in life was to grow up and be a mother.

There was a good chance that much of her adult life would be spent in pregnancy and childbirth and that she would die from some illness related to childbirth. In 1915, 61 women died per 10,000 live births in the United States. With today's advances in obstetrics and gynecology, only three women die per 10,000 live births. For every five girls born around 1900, about two could expect to reach the age of 65. For every five 20-year-old girls living today, about four can look forward to their 65th birthday.

Since women are living longer, they have many adult years to live when they are not predominantly concerned with having and rearing a family. In past centuries, the end of childbearing, menopause, came near the end of a woman's life. In this century a woman can expect to have 20 or more years beyond menopause to devote to her career, to her avocations, to her relationship with her husband.

It is a fact of woman's life that, when she marries and has children, she must accommodate her work life to the needs of her children and husband. If she is to have a career at all, she must have the help of her husband, her doctor, her community, and the schools in raising her children. More than ever before, fortunately, men are joining their wives in the practical work of raising a family —giving midnight bottles, diapering babies, doing the wash, babysitting while wives go to night school. Not all couples approve of or enjoy this new sharing of parental tasks. But a woman cannot expect to be both mother and worker without excellent assistance.

The day has passed when the man is viewed as the benevolent master of woman. Marriage seems to be approaching a true and equal partnership of the sexes. A 20-year-old friend once told me that he and his fiancee had decided to postpone their marriage until she had finished college and found a vocation to her liking. I told him that, considering how anxious he had been to get married, this was a generous concession on his part. "It's no concession," he replied. "She has the same right to fulfill her ambitions as I have to fulfill mine. I don't want to wake up some morning 20 years from now and hear her tell me I've taken the best years of her life."

5

How To Discuss Sex with Your Children

Where and when we discuss sex with our youngsters has a great deal to do with how easy our conversation will be. Naturally, one man's idea of comfort is another man's idea of cramped misery. I know a mother who finds driving a car the most comfortable way to talk at any length about sex and reproduction. When one of her children seems ready to go into details, she takes him for a drive in the country. I asked her if she isn't scared she might hit a car or wrap herself around a telephone pole. She answered, "Of course not. I don't drive over thirty miles an hour on those trips and I keep my eyes on the road. That's the whole point—if I have my eyes on the road, I don't have to look the kid straight in the face." Another mother told me that waxing floors on her hands and knees is the best arrangement for her. For fathers, puttering in the garage or basement may be the answer. Wherever it is, it should be somewhat secluded, so that people are not continually barging in and out and breaking up the continuity of the conversation. If your home is one of those where the phone is constantly ringing, try to get away from this source of interruption.

Although you want to find a comfortable, quiet place, you want to avoid making a "big deal" of your talks. Too much formal preparation or solemnity will kill any possibility for real communication. We surely do not want to put our youngsters through the strain of the dismal heart-to-heart talks we may have had with our own parents. If a mother gets up her courage and finally states, "Daughter, I want to talk with you about something very special," or the father declares, "Son, it's about time we had a man-to-man

talk," the youngster has every right to say, "Take it easy, let's have a talk when you're feeling better." As far as possible, our talks should be casual, everyday sorts of conversations. We don't want the youngster to think we are about to deliver a lecture on the fate of mankind or the inscrutable mysteries of life. Many, many questions demand only the shortest answers and can be answered at any time or place. For instance:

Child: Why is Mrs. Knight so fat?
Parent: She's going to have a baby.

Child: What's in that box?
Parent: Sanitary pads.

Child: Why do I look like Daddy instead of like you?
Parent: You got your looks from his side of the family.

If at all possible, you should answer every question, at least briefly, on the spot. Evasive answers carry the message, "Nice people don't talk about those things." And your child will be careful not to talk about "those things" again. If you are in a public place and feel as though everyone within earshot is listening to your conversation, give a brief answer and promise to go into details when you get home. The following interchange might take place at the check-out line in a supermarket:

Son: Mom, take a look at Mrs. Rand. Is she going to have a baby?

Mother: Yes. I thought you knew. I think it's due next month.

Son: She had twins last time. Will it be threes this time? Does it always get one more? Why wasn't I a twin?

40

Mother: No, it doesn't get one more each time. Anyway, it's not threes it's triplets. Will you *please* watch what you are doing and keep that cart in line. I'll tell you about twins when we get out of here.

If you do postpone a full discussion, make sure the topic is not left hanging in thin air. A youngster may seem to have forgotten the subject, but it's almost certain he hasn't. He may have been hesitant in bringing it up in the first place, and your postponement may have made him even more hesitant.

We should try not to overlook any of the invitations our youngsters give us to discuss sex and human reproduction. This frank questioning from our children is a compliment, because it means they feel sufficiently at ease with us to bring up these matters. Some parents have told me their children have never, never asked them a single question about sex. I wonder if these parents were truly listening for the questions. I have never met a child who wasn't curious—about everything, including sex. If I ever met one that wasn't, I would have to conclude that someone important to him had told him forcefully, though perhaps very, very subtly, that there are *some* things a child must never be curious about.

Answering the question

Parents are often disturbed by the *implications* of their children's questions rather than by the questions themselves. The child who asks "What is sexual intercourse?" will probably get a reasonable answer. If he uses a four-letter word to ask the same question, chances are he'll get an explosion. Yet the fact is that, for him, the four-letter word has no more meaning than the medical term; if it did, he probably wouldn't bother to ask. The best approach in this case, once you have your nerves under control, is to explain that the four-letter word is a crude word for sexual intercourse and to go on from there.

Sometimes we're tempted to answer questions the child *hasn't* asked, to give him more information than he asked for or wants. If the question "Does a stillborn baby mean a dead baby?" comes out of the blue, we may be tempted to go beyond a simple yes. But the fact that the thought of stillborn babies may provoke anxiety in us does not mean that it provokes anxiety in the child. In this instance, the child had already assimilated the fact that babies are sometimes born dead; it was the meaning of the word *stillborn* he was unsure of. All in all, it is better to let the child direct his education in sex. He knows what it is he wants to know, and when he wants to know it, he'll ask.

Conversations begin with listening

Sometimes we answer the wrong question because we weren't listening carefully enough when the question was asked. A student of mine told me of an experience she had when she was 11 years old. She had been menstruating for about a year when she suddenly missed a period. She had overheard a conversation between her parents about a missed period and the possibility of a new pregnancy, and so she asked her mother: "How would I know if I were pregnant?" Her mother, quite logically, replied, "Well, the surest sign would be if you stopped having your period." The girl spent the next month in absolute terror and agony, convinced that she was pregnant (even though she was still a virgin) until her next period began.

In this instance, the mother heard the *words* of the question, but was not listening closely enough to hear that the girl was asking a question about *herself*.

There is no doubt that listening—real listening—is demanding work. It means thinking about what's being said and the way it's being said. And there is no doubt that the best way to begin a conversation is to listen to what's being said or asked. If you know what your child's question means, as well as what it means to *him*, your answer will come easily and it will be the sort of answer he is looking for.

In the end, listening may simply mean staring into space for 10 or 20 seconds while you let the question sink in. Sometimes our listening silence can be misinterpreted by the youngster as rejection or disapproval. He may even say to you, when you are riveted on his every word, "What's the matter with you? Why don't you say something, anything?" And you can honestly answer, "Don't worry, I'll say something. Right now I'm busy thinking about what you're saying. I want to understand what you're saying."

Be prepared for ugly words and stories

It is a pity that, in English, we can generally choose only between the vocabulary of the gutter and the vocabulary of the medical textbook to discuss sex. *Vagina, penis, labia,* and the like have a stilted sound in our ears.

Of course, when our children speak, it isn't stilted language we have to worry about. Not having been exposed to the medical vocabulary, they must resort to the gutter vocabulary. Perhaps if we get used to the idea that they have no choice in this, we may find it easier to control our shock.

Children can generally tell when a word they've heard or seen belongs to the gutter vocabulary. People simply don't scrawl words like *labia* and *testicle* on bathroom walls. Knowing that many of the words for sexual organs and acts belong to the gutter, children can quite reasonably conclude that the organs and acts themselves belong to the gutter. This is why it is important to try to control our shock when our children use the only words that are available to them. If we overwhelm them with our disgust at hearing such words, they will probably be more convinced than ever that the things the words stand for must be disgusting as well.

Another reason for moderating our reaction is that children may also interpret our disgust for their language as disgust for them. It is as though we are saying: "How can a fine young person like you say such a thing—much less think about it?" We've simply got to try to remember that, to our innocent eight-year-old, sexual intercourse doesn't become a dirty act when it's spelled with four letters instead of 17.

There are times, of course, when it's what our child is actually saying, not merely his choice of words, that shocks us. Again, if we overwhelm him with our disgust, we merely create a new source of distress and confusion for him. Our best approach is probably something like, "Boy, that's quite a story. Let me see if I understand you correctly." The youngster will usually appreciate going over the ugly details of a sordid story with an understanding adult. Again, the key to a helpful discussion is our willingness to truly listen to what our youngster has to say. An interested "I see," a sincere "Really?" or even a sympathetic "Wow!" may be all he'll need in some very serious discussions. These small words make it possible for the youngster to talk. When we have a fairly good idea what is on the youngster's mind, we may be able to supply a needed interpretation or some missing factual information. A parent can feel truly complimented when his youngster gives a sigh of relief and says, "Oh, now I understand. I didn't get it before. You've cleared up a lot for me."

And what words do we use?

For the most part, our children want to know the "right" words for things, and they rely on us to supply them. When they learn the "right" word for a thing, it gains a bit of respectability in their eyes.

Children also want to learn the "right" words so that they'll have a vocabulary they can use when they talk to us. They'd have to be blind or stupid to miss the fact that we're uncomfortable with four-letter words.

And, finally, our younger children naturally tend to put us on pedestals and can be very hurt if we try to climb down. They expect us to use words that are appropriate to our lofty dignity. And, ironically, when they finally decide to push us off our pedestals, any attempt we make to use their language is likely to provoke a comment like "For heaven's sake, don't be foolish. Act your age."

In spite of all this, there are times when only a good, strong four-letter word will do to make a point, to clear the air, to bring a conversation down to earth. It is sometimes necessary to let your son or daughter know that you will not collapse in a heap if your child says the wrong word.

Keep it short and simple

People sometimes feel that ideas expressed in short, simple sentences cannot be as important or as valid as ideas expressed in weighty, complex sentences. Actually, the reverse is true. People generally resort to long words and contorted sentences only when they don't know their subject well enough to use short, simple ones.

Keeping it short and simple is especially important when we talk to our youngsters about sex and reproduction. An editor once asked me, "Do you mean to say that you can explain to a four-year-old how he was conceived? How could he understand it?" I answered, "It's not all that complicated. If it weren't simple to be conceived, you and I wouldn't be here." The facts of human reproduction are simple, and it's our job to keep them that way.

When we don't keep our answers short and simple, we run the risk of first giving the youngster a fact and then obscuring it in a cloud of explanation, examples, and exceptions. Give him the fact he wants. If he's satisfied with it, let it go at that. Unless he's ready for it, additional explanation will either confuse him or be ignored.

A short, simple answer can still be a complete answer. Of course, some complete answers are more complete than others. Again we can let the child himself decide how complete an answer he wants. Start with an outline covering only the major points.

This may be all he is looking for at the moment. Or he may want you to give a full description or to fill in one part of the outline.

Sometimes children are not sure what they're looking for. They may, for example, be fishing for some awful secret that simply doesn't exist. Many youngsters are certain that there are mysteries so well hidden that they haven't even heard the whispers. In a sense there *is* a mystery that can't be explained to them—the mysterious certainty that only direct experience of sex and reproduction can bring.

In your search for the short and simple answer, *The Life Cycle Library for Young People* should be of great help to you. These volumes contain hundreds of simple descriptions and diagrams dealing with bodily functions, sexual maturation, and human reproduction. Sometimes the most helpful response to a baffling question is: "I don't really know the answer to that one. Let's see if we can find out." I think you will discover that *The Life Cycle Library for Young People* is the book you are looking for.

The light touch

It's a good idea, when you've finished describing some organ or process to a child, to mentally replay your words to see what picture you have conveyed. You may find that you'll want to add something like, "That probably sounds pretty awful, but it really isn't. It's just that it's awkward trying to put it into words."

In addition to conveying misleading images about sex, we're apt to convey misleading attitudes about sex. Because we're worried about how well we're going to do as we talk and about our child's reaction, we're apt to lower our voices to a solemn level and wrinkle our brows in grave concentration, giving the impression that sex is a deadly serious business. As adults, we know that sex and reproduction are exciting, beautiful, and even funny aspects of life. It isn't easy to convey this to our children, but the more we try the easier it gets.

What comes after the facts?

Over and over again parents tell me they are not worried about getting across the facts about sex and reproduction. What worries them is getting across everything else—the feelings, the ideals, the moral principles. Somehow the younger children are only interested in the specifics of how, why, where, and when, while the older ones are inclined to dismiss our feelings, ideals, and moral principles as in a class with feather boas and antimacassars.

The fact is, however, that the feelings, ideals, and principles of parents do inevitably get across to children, whether they're put into words or not. The child who watches his father playing happily with the new infant understands his father's feelings about babies better than any words could convey. The child who catches his parents exchanging a sly wink knows more about their feelings toward each other than either could explain to him.

Like it or not, children draw their conclusions about life from watching us, not listening to us. If our lives show them the results of selfishness, cruelty, and pettiness, they are not likely to take us very seriously when we give them sermons about kindness and generosity. If our lives show kindness and generosity, sermons are not needed; they'll be sold without a word being said.

In our terrifically busy daily lives with our children we are constantly making choices—giving up this for that, weighing one alternative against another, deciding on one plan over another. It is from watching us make this enormous array of choices that children learn what we stand for and what we think is important. Our actions, much more than our words, spell out our feelings and our moral commitments.

Questions and answers

It is my impression that many parents find it difficult to talk to their children about the simplest facts of sexual development and human reproduction because they can't find the right words. We've been brought up with the notion that genteel breakfast conversations do not include questions like, "Daddy, why isn't my penis as big as yours?" Many aspects of sexual behavior and human reproduction are more or less taboo in some families. It's a pity, however, when modesty prevents adults and children from talking back and forth when they really want to. In reading the following 100 Questions and Answers, I think you will find avenues of discussion for you and your youngsters. I also think you'll be pleasantly surprised at how easily most questions can be answered. It is largely a matter of getting the words you already know from your brain to your mouth.

It must be remembered, at this point, that there is no one exactly right answer to any question. Your personality and your child's personality, the particular circumstances, the incident that raised the question, the current state of the child's information, and many other factors will influence your answer. In these 100 Questions and Answers I have only listed the most usual ways these questions are asked, and the most common correct answers. You and your children will undoubtedly have your own special way of saying the same things. My best advice is to remember to listen carefully to the question, so that you know what they are really asking, and then to keep the answer as short and simple as possible.

6

One Hundred Questions and Answers

Child birth

Where was I born?

You were born in Middleville Hospital. Babies are born in hospitals because the mother needs the help of the doctor and the nurses. Having a baby is not a sickness; it is a natural part of being a woman.

What is the maternity ward?

The maternity ward is the section of a hospital where a mother has her baby and stays for a few days after he's born. It's usually the happiest section of a hospital.

How was I born?

You were born when you came out of my body. You grew for about nine months inside my uterus before you were born.

What is labor? Do you go to work to have a baby?

It is hard work. At first you must wait while the uterus is pulling the cervix open. You can think of the cervix as the doorway between the uterus and the birth canal. You have to use all your muscles to push the baby down the birth canal and out into the world.

Who delivers a baby? What's a delivery?

People usually say that the doctor delivers the baby, but it's not like a mailman delivering a special delivery letter. The doctor helps the mother in the delivery of her baby, but she's the one who is doing the real work. When the baby actually comes out of the birth canal, you say he is being delivered.

What is the birth canal?

The birth canal is the vagina. The vagina is the passageway between the uterus and the outside of the body. It is called the birth canal because when a baby is born it passes through the vagina.

Can a woman train for having a baby the way an athlete trains for a track meet?

Certainly. There are special exercises that prepare pregnant women to use the muscles they need during childbirth.

Does it hurt to have a baby?

It hurts some. If a mother is well prepared for childbirth it need not be terribly painful. The doctor can help by giving the mother some pain-killing medicine. It also helps if she understands the whole process. Knowing what to expect actually makes it less painful.

What if it hurts a lot? I've heard that childbirth is the worst pain of all.

Yes, I know. Over the years women and men have been taught that childbirth is awful. But times have changed and doctors know much more than they used to. There are pain-killing drugs which a doctor can use to help a woman in labor and delivery. If you look at the faces of most women coming from the delivery room, you wouldn't think they'd had a very painful experience. Some look like they've just won a gold medal at the Olympics.

Did you see me being born?

No, I was too busy pushing. *Or:* Yes, they had a mirror above me so I could see you as you came out.

Did you know when I was born?

Yes. I was awake and heard you give your first cry. *Or:* No, I was still asleep; I saw you a little after you were born.

What is a Caesarean?

A Caesarean birth, or a C-section, is a surgical way to have a baby. Sometimes it isn't safe for mother or baby for birth to occur in the normal way. At the end of pregnancy the mother is prepared for surgery and given an anesthetic. The doctor makes a cut in the mother's belly and lifts the baby out. He stitches the cut closed and soon it heals. This operation is safe and a woman can have as many babies as she wants in this way.

Why does a new baby's head look so funny?

A baby's head is not completely solid bone. It has to be flexible, because there is great pressure on the baby while he is being pushed out. The head gets back to its normal shape a week or so after birth.

Prenatal development ——————————————————

How did I eat before I was born?

You didn't eat the way you do now. Your nourishment came to you through the umbilical cord, which was attached to you at your belly-button. The umbilical cord was attached to a special organ in the uterus called the placenta. The placenta is a bit like a lunch counter. The baby's blood flows through the umbilical cord to the placenta, picks up nourishment, oxygen, and water, and then flows back to the baby.

When I was inside of you did I sleep?

Sure you did. You slept very much the way a newborn baby does. You also moved and kicked when you heard a loud noise. Sometimes you moved around so much I couldn't get to sleep.

Is it safe for a baby to live inside his mother? Doesn't he get moved around an awful lot?

It's just about the safest place a baby can grow. From the moment life begins the baby floats in a warm water bath and is well protected from bumps and crashes.

How does a baby breathe if he's floating in water before he's born?

He doesn't breathe the way we do. He gets all the oxygen he needs through the umbilical card. His lungs develop, but he doesn't use them to breathe air until he's born. A baby's first cry on being born is exciting because it's his first breath of air.

What is a belly button for?

A belly button is where the umbilical cord was attached before you were born. After you were born the doctor cut the cord and left a small stump on your belly. The stump fell off and left you with a belly button.

What is an abortion?

To have an abortion means to have a miscarriage or to stop a pregnancy. In a miscarriage, the baby can't continue to develop for one reason or another, and so it dies and is expelled from the mother's body. When you stop a pregnancy, it's called a therapeutic abortion, meaning that it's done for a medical reason. In most places in the world it's against the law to have an abortion without having a medical reason for it.

Can you find out the sex of a new baby before he's born?

Yes, there is a test that can be used, but it's not done very often.

How is a baby's sex determined?

The baby's sex is determined by the father's sperm at the instant of conception. The mother's egg cell does not determine the sex of the baby.

Fertilization

What are sex glands?

Sex glands are the glands that regulate sexual development and reproduction. Male sex glands are called testicles and are outside the body, behind the penis. Female sex glands are called ovaries and are inside the body. The testicles and the ovaries contain germ cells.

What is a germ cell?

A germ cell is not a germ. It is a reproductive or sex cell. In the man, the germ cell is the sperm. In the woman, it is the ovum, or egg cell. Every baby begins from a sperm cell and an egg cell.

How does the sperm get to the egg cell?

It swims there. During sexual intercourse, the man deposits millions of sperm in the woman's vagina. The sperm travel through the cervix, into the uterus, and finally into the Fallopian tubes, where one may join an egg.

You mean a man actually puts his penis inside a woman's body?

Yes, that's the way human beings are made. Our bodies are constructed so that a man and a woman fit together beautifully. Husband and wife are really made for each other.

Does it take only one egg and one sperm to begin a baby?

Exactly. When your life began, you were the size of a very small dot. We don't know how it happens, but when a sperm enters an egg, the egg closes itself off so that no more sperm can enter.

What happens to the rest of the sperm?

They die and disintegrate after about three days.

Since there are so many sperm, why aren't there lots of twins and triplets?

It's true there are millions of sperm in one teaspoon of semen, but there is usually only one egg for all those sperm to fertilize. Once in a great while, a woman's ovary discharges two eggs instead of one, and then there may be *fraternal* twins. Even more rarely, the fertilized egg may divide and develop into two *identical* twins. Since identical twins develop from the same egg and sperm, they are very much alike. Fraternal twins develop from different eggs and different sperm, and so are no more alike than ordinary brothers or sisters.

Is it possible to begin a baby without sexual intercourse?

Yes, it can happen, but very rarely. If a man ejaculates near the opening of the vagina, even if his penis has not gone in, it is possible—though unlikely—for the sperm to work their way up through the vagina and then into the Fallopian tubes.

What is making love?

Making love is another term for having sexual intercourse.

What is an orgasm? What does it mean to "come"?

An orgasm is the peak or climax of sexual excitement. A man "comes"—has an orgasm—when he ejaculates. A woman may have several orgasms during love-making—before, during, or after the man's orgasm. A woman does not have to have an orgasm to become pregnant.

What is necking?

Necking is kissing and holding hands. Some people have said it is making love above the neck.

What is petting?

Petting is fondling, caressing, and making love without having sexual intercourse. Sexual intercourse is usually preceded by petting.

What is copulation?

Copulation is another term for mating or sexual intercourse. Human beings and most animals copulate.

Do animals mate the same way human beings do?

Physically, yes, but in all other ways it's completely different. Men and women feel love, affection, and tenderness for each other, and love-making has a great deal of meaning and importance that mating doesn't have for animals. On the whole, it's more different than alike.

What does it mean to reproduce?

To reproduce means to make another like yourself—to have a baby. All living things reproduce.

What is family planning?

Family planning is another term for birth control. When a married couple decides how many babies to have and when to have them, they are practicing family planning.

What is the Pill?

The Pill is a method of birth control that stops ovulation and therefore makes it impossible for a woman to conceive.

Male reproductive system

What is a penis?

A penis is a man's sex organ. It hangs on the outside of his body and is about the size and shape of a large thumb.

If urine and semen both pass through the penis, how are they kept from mixing?

A valve automatically shuts off the urine during an erection. Even if he wants to, a man cannot urinate when the penis is erect.

What are the testicles?

The testicles are the man's reproductive glands. They are two small balls which hang in a sac behind the penis. The testicles produce sperm.

Does the size of a man's penis tell you anything about his masculinity?

No. A big penis does not mean a man has a more-than-average sex urge. A small penis does not mean a man is not virile or masculine.

What causes an erection?

The penis becomes enlarged and erect when the blood vessels in the penis are filled with an extra supply of blood. This is usually caused by sexual excitement, but it can also be caused by a full bladder or by almost any kind of excitement.

What is an ejaculation?

An ejaculation is a discharge of semen from the penis. Semen is a milky fluid that contains millions of sperm, the male sex cell.

Does a man or boy have an ejaculation every time he has an erection?

No, a man and especially a young boy or young man has many erections in which there is no ejaculation. There cannot, however, be an ejaculation without an erection.

When does a man ejaculate?

The most usual time is when he is at a peak of sexual excitement. The main purpose of an ejaculation is to get the male sex cell into contact with a female sex cell.

Is a man weakened by having an ejaculation?

No, he is not weakened in any way. Once a young man becomes sexually mature he produces a never-ending supply of sperm.

What is a wet dream?

A wet dream is an ejaculation during sleep. The wet dream—or nocturnal emission—is the body's way of discharging an unneeded supply of semen. It's called a wet *dream* because the ejaculation is often accompanied by a sexually exciting dream.

Can a boy become a father once he has begun to have wet dreams?

Yes, the sperm in any ejaculation are capable of beginning a baby. Of course a wet dream alone cannot cause a conception. To begin a baby, the sperm must be deposited in a fertile woman's vagina so that the sperm can reach an egg cell.

Do all men and boys have wet dreams?

Yes, this is nature's way of disposing of extra semen. Most boys begin to have wet dreams between the ages of 12 and 16.

Can a man have a baby?

No, a man cannot have a baby. A man's body is not made to develop a baby within him. The father is essential, of course, because he begins the baby, but it is the mother who carries the baby within her for nine months and then gives birth.

Female reproductive system

Do girls have penises? Did they have them when they were born and then lose them?

No, girls don't have penises and they never did. Boys are born with penises so that they can someday put sperm into a woman's vagina. Women are born with vaginas and wombs so that they can someday receive sperm and have babies.

How does a woman urinate?

A woman urinates from a small hole in her vulva. She simply sits on a toilet and releases the urine when she senses her bladder is full.

What is the vulva?

The vulva is the genital area of a woman and is between her legs. The vulva is made up of inner and outer lips. At the front end of the vulva is the clitoris. Behind the clitoris is the urethra from which a woman urinates. The vaginal opening is within the vulva.

Why do girls have breasts?

Humans are mammals, and mammals feed their babies with their own milk. Breasts fill up with milk after the baby is born and are a perfect supply of clean, warm nourishment.

What are nipples for?

The mother's milk comes through the nipples when the baby sucks. A woman's nipples are sensitive to touch. They stand up, become erect, when she is sexually excited.

Does the size of a woman's breasts tell you if she can breast feed?

No. The size of the breasts does not determine milk supply. A woman with small breasts can have lots of milk.

Does it hurt the mother when she breast feeds?

No, in the early months the baby has no teeth. Nursing a baby feels good to the mother.

What is the clitoris?

The clitoris is a small nub of flesh at the front of the vulva. It becomes enlarged and erect when the woman is sexually excited and is a center of sexual pleasure.

What is the vagina?

The vagina is the passageway between the uterus and the outside of the body. The vagina is the birth canal, and menstrual blood passes through the vagina. During sexual intercourse, the man places his penis in the vagina.

What is a uterus?

The uterus is an internal organ that is hollow and very elastic. A baby grows in the uterus before it is born.

What are the Fallopian tubes?

The Fallopian tubes are two canals in a woman's body leading from the ovaries to the top of the uterus. One end of each tube is near an ovary. When the ovary releases an egg, it travels down one of the Fallopian tubes. Fertilization usually takes place in one of the tubes.

What is an ovary?

An ovary is the female sex gland, located inside the body, near the uterus. Every woman has two ovaries. They secrete hormones that control the woman's reproductive cycle. When a woman becomes sexually mature, each ovary discharges an egg every other month.

What is the hymen?

The hymen is a thin membrane which partially blocks the entrance to the vagina. There is a hole in the membrane which permits blood to flow out of the body during menstruation.

How can you tell if a girl is a virgin?

You can't. In the past, people reasoned this way: If a girl's hymen is intact, she's a virgin; if it's not intact, she's not a virgin. It's true that a girl whose hymen is intact is a virgin, because sexual intercourse tears the hymen. But it's *not* true that a girl whose hymen is torn has necessarily lost her virginity. The hymen can be torn in other ways besides sexual intercourse—by strenuout activity or by the use of tampons.

Menstruation

What is menstruation?

Every month, a woman's uterus prepares to receive a fertilized egg. It does this by building up a lining of blood. If the woman's egg is fertilized, it lodges in this lining to grow. If it isn't fertilized, the lining of the uterus isn't needed and the body discharges it in the form of a bloody fluid. This discharge is called menstruation.

Is it safe to take a bath when you're menstruating?

It's perfectly safe. A warm bath or shower every day keeps you feeling fresh and clean.

What's the "curse"? What's "ladies' day"? What's "falling off the roof"?

These are all slang expressions for menstruation. They give the impression that there's something wrong with menstruation, but menstruation is a natural and healthy process.

What are cramps?

When a woman or girl talks about cramps she usually means menstrual cramps. Some women experience aches and pains when they menstruate. These are most likely to occur during the first few days of menstruation.

What are the "leaks" or the "whites"?

These are slang words for leukorrhea, a discharge from the vagina. The discharge may be perfectly normal or a sign of an infection. It is normal to have a slight discharge before and after menstruation. The vagina also becomes moist when a woman is sexually aroused.

Pregnancy

How can you tell you are pregnant?

The most reliable sign of pregnancy is when you've stopped menstruating for a couple of months in a row. Other signs of pregnancy are fatigue and enlargement of the breasts.

What is morning sickness?

A pregnant woman sometimes feels sick to her stomach in the morning. Morning sickness usually stops after the third month of pregnancy.

When a woman is pregnant, does the menstrual blood go each month to the baby in her uterus?

No. When a woman is pregnant menstruation stops. A system develops between the mother and the growing baby which allows the baby to manufacture his own blood. The mother's blood and the baby's blood never mix directly.

Can a woman have sexual intercourse when she is pregnant? What happens if she starts a second baby while the first one is still growing in her uterus?

A woman can have sexual intercourse almost all the time when she is pregnant. Once she becomes pregnant, she stops ovulating, and so she can't conceive again during pregnancy.

When can I have a baby? Can children have babies?

No, children can't have babies. Men and women have to be sexually mature to have babies.

Are women fertile all their lives?

No, women are usually only fertile between the ages of 14 and 45, approximately. Around age 45, women stop menstruating and experience menopause. During menopause, their bodies change and they are no longer capable of having babies.

Can a woman have a baby without being married?

Yes. A woman may be widowed or divorced while she's pregnant. Or she may not have been married when she became pregnant. If she doesn't get married before the baby is born, she'll be an unwed mother. That can be pretty difficult for her.

Sexual problems

What is a bastard?

A bastard is an illegitimate child. An illegitimate baby is a child born to parents who are not legally married to each other. If a baby is conceived *before* they're married but born *after* they're married, it is a legitimate baby, not a bastard.

What is castration?

First of all, castration is *not* circumcision. They may sound alike, but they are completely different. Castration is the loss of the testicles by accident or surgery.

What is circumcision?

Circumcision is the removal of the foreskin, a loose piece of skin at the end of the penis. This operation is usually performed a few days after birth. Since it's easier to keep the penis clean if the foreskin is removed, doctors generally recommend it, but they leave it to the parents to decide whether their boy should be circumcized.

What is a prostitute?

A prostitute is a person who has sexual relations for money.

What is VD?

VD are initials which stand for venereal disease. Venereal diseases are diseases contracted through sexual intercourse. The two most common types of VD in the United States are gonorrhea and syphilis.

What is a prophylactic?

Anything that is used to guard against disease can be called a prophylactic. The word most usually means a way of preventing VD.

What is adultery? Is it adults having sexual intercourse?

No. Adultery is sexual intercourse when one or both persons are married but not to each other.

What is incest?

Incest is having sexual intercourse with a close relative of the opposite sex. All religions forbid sexual relations between members of the same family (other than husband and wife).

What is impotence?

Impotence is the inability to have an erection. Impotence usually has an emotional cause, and most men have been impotent at one time or another.

What is a homosexual?

A homosexual is a person who prefers having sexual relations with a person of the same sex. Heterosexuals are persons who prefer to have sexual relations with persons of the opposite sex.

Are people born homosexual?

No. Life experiences in childhood probably cause homosexuality.

Can a person change from being homosexual to being heterosexual?

Yes. If a person really wants to change his sexual feelings he may be helped by psychological therapy.

There's a boy in my class who behaves a lot like a girl. He's sort of prissy and giggly. Is he a homosexual?

Not necessarily. Boys sometimes go through a period in which they have girlish mannerisms.

What is a frigid woman?

A frigid woman is one who has little interest in or desire for sexual pleasure. Frigidity is usually a psychological problem, rather than a physical one, and can often be reduced with psychological help.

What is rape?

Rape is sexual intercourse forced on a person who does not want to have intercourse.

What is premarital intercourse? What are premarital relations?

When a couple have sexual intercourse before they are married, they are having premarital intercourse, or premarital relations.

Can you eat something special to make your penis or your breasts get larger?

No. The size and shape of your body is mostly determined by inheritance.

What is masturbation?

Masturbation is rubbing the genitals and getting pleasure from the sensation. A boy or man rubs his penis and testicles, a girl or woman rubs her vulva and clitoris.

What is pornography?

Pornographic materials—films, books, pictures, and so forth—are materials created for the sole purpose of arousing a person sexually.

What does erotic mean?

Erotic means "having to do with sexual love." Many poets and painters have created erotic works. The difference between these works and pornographic works is that the pornographic works are not artistically pleasing—they're just supposed to be sexually arousing.

Love

What is love?

There are many, many ideas about what love is. To some people, love is only what happens to you when you've "fallen in love"—that delicious experience of finding the one perfect person in the world for you. The trouble is that this sort of rapture doesn't last, whereas mature love does. People who love in a mature way know that the one they love isn't absolutely perfect—but they still love him or her. They want to be near that person, to live and grow with that person. That person makes them feel alive and complete.

What is infatuation?

Infatuation is what happens when you fall so hard for someone that you lose all sense of proportion. When you're infatuated with someone, that person seems to be the absolute epitome of wit, wisdom, and beauty, and you feel that the entire universe would collapse into nothingness if you were ever parted.

How will I know when it's love?

You have to get over being infatuated with a person before you can be sure. It's easy to be fooled when the sky is filled with heavenly choirs. If the choirs have disappeared and you'd *still* rather be with this person than with anyone else in the world, then chances are good that it's the real thing.